LESBIAN SURVIVAL HINT #96:

ALTHOUGH OUR TASTES AND STATUS
MAY CHANGE, THE POTLUCK
IS WITH US TO STAY.

THE LESBIAN SURVIVAL MANUAL

CARTOONS BY RHONDA DICKSION

The Naiad Press, Inc.
1990

Printed in the United States of America
First Edition

Cover design by Pat Tong and Bonnie Liss
    (Phoenix Graphics)
Typeset by Sandi Stancil

Library of Congress Cataloging-in-Publication Data

Dicksion, Rhonda, 1959—
    Lesbian survival manual / by Rhonda Dicksion.
        p.   cm.
    ISBN 0-941483-71-1
    1. Lesbians--Caricatures and cartoons. 2. American wit and
humor. Pictorial. I. Title.
NC 1429.D45A4   1990
741.5'973--dc20
                                                                90-6133
                                                                CIP

This book is dedicated lovingly
(though certainly not *with a "straight" face),*
to
Krysta Gibson

ABOUT THE AUTHOR

Rhonda Dicksion is a cartoonist who lives, loves and draws on her experience in the wild outskirts of Seattle. A Southern California native, Rhonda was raised by patient and understanding parents who kept her in crayons and didn't mind repainting the nursery walls.

Setting aside a promising career doing murals, she opted instead for cartooning. She maintains that for her cartooning is a way of life. "I know cartooning must seem tough to most people . . . sitting on the porch in the sun thinking; spending late nights at nightclubs researching; endlessly watching videos while inking . . . but I feel in some way that these small sacrifices are worth the effort."

Thanks:

To Joan, who claims she taught me how
to do it;

To June, who kept me up while doing it;

To Carolyn, Elaine, Libby & Carol who told
me how they thought I could do it better;

To Jane, who gave me the confidence
to do it in public;

To Barbara, who told me I could
do it nationwide;

To Wendy & Dennis, who let me
do it at work;

To all the people who laugh when I do it;

And especially to Sparky and The Cats, who
have given me the love, space — and
inspiration — to do it.

Mirthfully,

Rhonda

LESBIAN SURVIVAL HINT # 30:
LOVE HER — LOVE HER CATS.

LESBIAN SURVIVAL HINT #61:

CELEBRATE THE HALLMARKS
OF YOUR RELATIONSHIPS.

LESBIAN SURVIVAL HINT #100:

SOME OF HUMANITY'S GREATEST MYSTERIES ARE EASILY UNRAVELED WHEN PUT INTO PROPER PERSPECTIVE.

LESBIAN SURVIVAL HINT #64:

REMEMBER THAT HENS
DON'T NEED ROOSTERS, EITHER.

LESBIAN SURVIVAL HINT #74:

A CLUTTERED BED MAY RUIN AN
OTHERWISE ROMANTIC EVENING.

LESBIAN SURVIVAL HINT # 54:

BE READY FOR THAT INEVITABLE CALL
FROM THE PRINCIPAL ABOUT YOUR
DAUGHTER PLAYING "AMAZONS AND
THE PATRIARCHY" DURING RECESS.

LESBIAN SURVIVAL HINT #56:

IF YOU LOVE SOMEONE, YOU CAN
OVERLOOK HER PAST BAD HABITS.

LESBIAN SURVIVAL HINT #51:

REMEMBER THAT SOME WOMEN'S
PRE-REQUISITES MAY
JUST BE TOO TOUGH.

LESBIAN SURVIVAL HINT #38:

IN A SCENARIO SUCH AS THIS, DON'T EVEN ATTEMPT ARGUING — THE CAT WILL ALWAYS COME UP SMELLING LIKE A ROSE.

LESBIAN SURVIVAL HINT #44:
COMPROMISE CAN KILL.

LESBIAN SURVIVAL HINT #11:

"SISTERS" MAY OFTEN BE IDENTIFIED
BY THEIR FOOTWEAR.

LESBIAN SURVIVAL HINT #106:

IF YOU WANT HER TO HELP CLEAN,
THERE'S ONE WHITE LIE
THAT NEVER FAILS...

LESBIAN SURVIVAL HINT # 62:
PRIDE GO-ETH BEFORE THE FALL.

LESBIAN SURVIVAL HINT #29:

SUPPORT YOUR LOCAL NIGHTSPOT.

LESBIAN SURVIVAL HINT #33:

A "SUNDAY AFTERNOON HUDDLE"
MAY NOT BE EXACTLY WHAT
YOU'D HOPED IT WOULD BE.

LESBIAN SURVIVAL HINT #79:

TO SOME WOMEN "DYKE" WILL ALWAYS BE A FOUR-LETTER WORD.

LESBIAN SURVIVAL HINT #125:

SOMETIMES HAVING A REPUTATION
CAN BE A PAIN IN THE NECK.

LESBIAN SURVIVAL HINT #81:

DON'T FIGHT THE URGE
TO BE A REBEL—
IT'S BORN INTO THE BLOOD.

LESBIAN SURVIVAL HINT #122:

ONE OF THE BEST THINGS ABOUT OUR
RELATIONSHIPS IS THAT YOUR PARTNER
PROBABLY HATES FOR YOU TO DIET
AS MUCH AS YOU DO.

LESBIAN SURVIVAL HINT #95:

FLATTERY <u>CAN</u> GET YOU EVERYWHERE, BUT BE SURE TO STICK TO THE SAFEST BODY PARTS.

LESBIAN SURVIVAL HINT #22:

IF HER BEAR IS IN DIAPERS AND SHE'S
OGLING THE TURKEY BASTER,
MATERNITY CLOTHES
MAY BE IN YOUR FUTURE.

LESBIAN SURVIVAL HINT #31:
BREAK IT TO MOM GENTLY.

LESBIAN SURVIVAL HINT #98:

IF YOU OPEN A CAN OF WORMS, YOU'D
BETTER BE PREPARED TO EAT THEM.

LESBIAN SURVIVAL HINT #82:
RESPECT EACH OTHER'S RITES.

LESBIAN SURVIVAL HINT #78:

ALTHOUGH DELICIOUS, HOT FUDGE
MAY NOT BE THE SAFEST TOPPING.

LESBIAN SURVIVAL HINT #10:

NEVER, EVER
RUN AFOUL OF THE LESBIAN POLICE.

LESBIAN SURVIVAL HINT #9:

BEFORE YOU BECOME INVOLVED, FIND
OUT WHAT SHE MEANS
BY MENAGE A TROIS.

LESBIAN SURVIVAL HINT #84:
THERE'S BUTCH, AND THEN THERE'S **BUTCH**.

LESBIAN SURVIVAL HINT #III:

ISN'T IT COMFORTING TO KNOW THAT
THERE IS OTHER
INTELLIGENT LIFE OUT THERE?

LESBIAN SURVIVAL HINT #109:

YOU CAN ALWAYS SPOT THE NOVICE
ON HER FIRST TIME OUT.

LESBIAN SURVIVAL HINT #80:

IT'S EASIER TO FACE A DIET
IF YOU DO IT WITH
A LIKE-MINDED FRIEND.

LESBIAN SURVIVAL HINT #46:

IT'S USUALLY RELATIVELY SIMPLE TO
TELL WHEN
YOUR ROOMATE'S IN LOVE AGAIN.

LESBIAN SURVIVAL HINT #96:

ALTHOUGH OUR TASTES AND STATUS
MAY CHANGE, THE POTLUCK
IS WITH US TO STAY.

LESBIAN SURVIVAL HINT #114:

NICKNAMES CAN TELL YOU A LOT
ABOUT A PERSON.

LESBIAN SURVIVAL HINT #66:

THERE IS SOMEBODY BEHIND EVERY
BAD IDEA—AND MOST
LIKELY IT ISN'T A WOMAN.

LESBIAN SURVIVAL HINT #14:

ENDURING LOVE IS WHEN YOU CAN
STILL LEER AT EACH OTHER NO MATTER
WHAT ACTIVITIES YOU'RE ENGAGED IN.

LESBIAN SURVIVAL HINT #77:

YOU MAY FIND THAT YOUR SOCIAL
CALENDAR FILLS UP MORE QUICKLY
WHEN YOU CLEAN OUT
YOUR BACKPACK REGULARLY.

LESBIAN SURVIVAL HINT #68:

DISABILITY IS IN THE
EYES OF THE BEHOLDER.

LESBIAN SURVIVAL HINT #41:

DEVELOPING EFFECTIVE COMMUNICATION
IS THE KEY TO A
SUCCESSFUL RELATIONSHIP.

LESBIAN SURVIVAL HINT #113:

BE PREPARED FOR THE OLD
"GREEN-EYED MONSTER" TO STRIKE.

LESBIAN SURVIVAL HINT #105:

IN TIMES OF STRESS, A GOOD SUPPORT
NETWORK IS INVALUABLE.

LESBIAN SURVIVAL HINT # 89:

CAMOUFLAGE IS OFTEN ONE
OF OUR GREATEST WEAPONS.

LESBIAN SURVIVAL HINT #36:

THE INNOVATIVE WOMAN CAN ALWAYS
FIND A JOB THAT COMBINES HER
PROFESSIONAL AND PERSONAL INTERESTS.

LESBIAN SURVIVAL HINT #115:

WHEN OUT STROLLING ON A STORMY
DAY, USE ONLY ONE UMBRELLA.

LESBIAN SURVIVAL HINT #37:

REMEMBER—ONE IN TEN WOMEN ARE GAY, BUT THE OTHER NINE ARE SURE THAT THEY'RE THERAPISTS.

LESBIAN SURVIVAL HINT #110:

IT'S PERFECTLY ACCEPTABLE TO CARRY
A PURSE— AS LONG AS IT
LOOKS LIKE A BACKPACK.

LESBIAN SURVIVAL HINT #86:

SOMETIMES IT MAY NOT BE TO YOUR OWN BEST ADVANTAGE TO BE CHEM-FREE AND POLITICALLY CORRECT.

LESBIAN SURVIVAL HINT #19:

BE SURE TO TAKE THE FIELD-GLASSES
WHEN ATTEMPTING
TO LOCATE A GAY BAR.

LESBIAN SURVIVAL HINT #87:

REMEMBER, YOU ARE NOT
A "DOWNTRODDEN MINORITY"—
YOU ARE A "PRIVILEDGED ELITE."

LESBIAN SURVIVAL HINT #3:

SOME CROSSES ARE EASIER
TO BEAR THAN OTHERS.

LESBIAN SURVIVAL HINT #96:

TRUE INTIMACY IS WHEN YOU CAN'T
TELL WHOSE SOCKS ARE WHOSE.

LESBIAN SURVIVAL HINT #108:

SIMPLY REFRAINING FROM CLOSE
PHYSICAL CONTACT CAN KEEP YOU
FROM CATCHING HER COLD.

LESBIAN SURVIVAL HINT #45:

IF SHE INVITES YOU OUT TO LISTEN TO
SOME MUSIC, BE SURE
YOU'RE CLEAR ON WHAT TYPE.

LESBIAN SURVIVAL HINT #35:

SOMETIMES IT TAKES RAW COURAGE
TO FOLLOW YOUR DREAM.

LESBIAN SURVIVAL HINT #116:

IT'S NOT SO MUCH THE FLOWERS AS
HOW YOU DELIVER THEM
THAT WILL GET YOU IN THE DOOR.

LESBIAN SURVIVAL HINT #72:

BE PREPARED FOR THE PATRIARCHY'S
LITTLE DISCOURAGEMENTS.

LESBIAN SURVIVAL HINT #52:

MAY-DECEMBER RELATIONSHIPS
HAVE THEIR OWN
SPECIAL ADVANTAGES.

LESBIAN SURVIVAL HINT #57:

THE LESBIAN OF THE 90s APPROACHES
HER RELATIONSHIPS
IN A CALM, PROFESSIONAL MANNER.

LESBIAN SURVIVAL HINT #75:

ON TRIPS TO THE BACK-COUNTRY, IT
IS ALWAYS PRUDENT
TO PACK TWO FLASHLIGHTS.

LESBIAN SURVIVAL HINT #60:

WHEN YOU BRING HOME A NEW
FRIEND TO WATCH T.V., MAKE SURE
THE SEATING IS ADEQUATE.

LESBIAN SURVIVAL HINT #34:

SOMETIMES MARRIAGE MEANS
A RETURN TO THE CLOSET.

LESBIAN SURVIVAL HINT #23:

ALWAYS KEEP SOME SPARE PACKAGES
HANDY TO KEEP
IN THE PASSENGER SEAT.

LESBIAN SURVIVAL HINT #133:

NEVER TRUST
THIRD-HAND INFORMATION.

LESBIAN SURVIVAL HINT #115:
THERE ARE MANY TYPES OF TIES
THAT BIND.

LESBIAN SURVIVAL HINT #18:

BE WARY OF FORM LETTERS.

LESBIAN SURVIVAL HINT #39:

THE COMMITMENT CEREMONY SHOULD
REFLECT OUR DEAREST
BELIEFS AND VALUES.

LESBIAN SURVIVAL HINT #90:

DON'T CALL IN SICK—JUST TELL THE BOSS
YOU'RE STAYING HOME TO WORK ON
YOUR "USER-FRIENDLY COMPATIBLE."

LESBIAN SURVIVAL HINT #92:

LET IT COME AS NO SURPRISE THAT
WE OFTEN HAVE TROUBLE
WITH MALE CO-WORKERS.

LESBIAN SURVIVAL HINT #93:

HAVING DEPILATORIES ON HAND CAN
HELP YOU STAY AFLOAT ON THE EVER-
TURNING TIDE
OF POLITICAL CORRECTNESS.

LESBIAN SURVIVAL HINT #117:

IT IS WISE FOR POTENTIAL PARTNERS
TO SHARE THE SAME CONCEPT
OF "STOCKS AND BONDS."

LESBIAN SURVIVAL HINT #26:

IF SHE DRIVES RIGHT PAST YOU
WITHOUT WAVING,
THERE'S PROBABLY A REASON.

LESBIAN SURVIVAL HINT #12:

WHEN OUT IN PUBLIC, BEAR IN MIND
THAT IT OFTEN MAKES STRAIGHTS SICK
TO SEE US
FLAUNT OUR SEXUALITY.

LESBIAN SURVIVAL HINT #21:

THE ONLY SUBJECT WE TEND TO
DISAGREE ON, IS THE ONE WE ARE
DISCUSSING AT THE MOMENT.

LESBIAN SURVIVAL HINT #55:

IF YOU COME OUT AT WORK,
BE PREPARED
TO ACCEPT THE CONSEQUENCES.

LESBIAN SURVIVAL HINT #28:

SOMETIMES IT CAN BE
FUN AND ENTERTAINING TO PLAY THE
"WEAKER SEX" GAME.

LESBIAN SURVIVAL HINT # 53:

REMEMBER THAT NOT ALL SISTERS
ARE AS SPIRITUALLY AWARE
AS OTHERS.

LESBIAN SURVIVAL HINT #104:

THERE ARE WORSE THINGS THAN
FINDING YOURSELF AT CAMP.

LESBIAN SURVIVAL HINT #8:

WHEN YOU COME OUT TO YOUR MOM, DON'T BE SURPRISED IF SHE TELLS YOU SHE ALREADY KNEW.

LESBIAN SURVIVAL HINT #71:

PROCEED WITH CAUTION IF SHE TELLS
YOU SHE KNOWS
WHERE YOU CAN GET SOME WACS.

LESBIAN SURVIVAL HINT #17:

IT SHOULD COME AS NO SURPRISE
THAT BIKING IS SO POPULAR.

LESBIAN SURVIVAL HINT #48:

IF FLIRTING IS HER PROBLEM,
GENTLY HELP HER CONTROL IT.

LESBIAN SURVIVAL HINT #65:

"WINING AND DINING" MEANS
DIFFERENT THINGS
TO DIFFERENT PEOPLE.

LESBIAN SURVIVAL HINT #85:
DIVIDE HOUSEHOLD CHORES EQUALLY.

LESBIAN SURVIVAL HINT #16:

USE HER UNFAMILIARITY WITH THE
INTERNAL COMBUSTION ENGINE
TO YOUR OWN BEST ADVANTAGE.

LESBIAN SURVIVAL HINT #40:

REMEMBER, WHEN PURCHASING ART
FOR THE HOME, ABSTRACTS DO NOT
HAVE TO BE REMOVED
WHEN PARENTS COME TO VISIT.

LESBIAN SURVIVAL HINT #101:

IF ANY OF THE ABOVE CRITERIA
    DESCRIBES YOU, YOU MAY
BE JUDGED POLITICALLY INCORRECT.

LESBIAN SURVIVAL HINT # 128:

THE AVERAGE LESBIAN IS QUITE ADEPT AT FINDING EXTRAORDINARY USES FOR COMMON HOUSEHOLD OBJECTS.

LESBIAN SURVIVAL HINT #97:

SOMETIMES IT DOESN'T TAKE MUCH
DIGGING TO FIND
A HIDDEN AGENDA.

LESBIAN SURVIVAL HINT #129:

YOU CAN FIND AFFIRMATION FOR
YOUR LIFESTYLE FROM
THE MOST UNLIKELY SOURCES.

LESBIAN SURVIVAL HINT #20:

REMEMBER THAT IN MANY INSTANCES
THE STORY WE WERE TOLD IS THE
WAY THE BOYS WANTED US TO HEAR IT.

LESBIAN SURVIVAL HINT #70:

BEFORE YOU GIVE HER AN ULTIMATUM
ABOUT HER CATS,
LOCATE YOUR SUITCASE.

LESBIAN SURVIVAL HINT #107:

MANY WOMEN PREFER HAVING A
VICE TO THE AIMLESSNESS
OF A CLEAN LIFESTYLE.

LESBIAN SURVIVAL HINT #49:

THE "LESBIAN POLICE"
SHOULD NOT BE YOUR ONLY CONCERN.

LESBIAN SURVIVAL HINT #69.

THERE'S SOMETHING I'VE BEEN MEANING TO TELL
YOU Ed. by Loralee MacPike. 288 pp. Gay men and lesbians
coming out to their children. ISBN 0-941483-44-4 9.95
ISBN 0-941483-54-1 16.95

LIFTING BELLY by Gertrude Stein. Ed. by Rebecca Mark. 104
pp. Erotic poetry. ISBN 0-941483-51-7 8.95
ISBN 0-941483-53-3 14.95

ROSE PENSKI by Roz Perry. 192 pp. Adult lovers in a long-term
relationship. ISBN 0-941483-37-1 8.95

AFTER THE FIRE by Jane Rule. 256 pp. Warm, human novel
by this incomparable author. ISBN 0-941483-45-2 8.95

SUE SLATE, PRIVATE EYE by Lee Lynch. 176 pp. The gay
folk of Peacock Alley are *all* cats. ISBN 0-941483-52-5 8.95

CHRIS by Randy Salem. 224 pp. Golden oldie. Handsome Chris
and her adventures. ISBN 0-941483-42-8 8.95

THREE WOMEN by March Hastings. 232 pp. Golden oldie. A
triangle among wealthy sophisticates. ISBN 0-941483-43-6 8.95

RICE AND BEANS by Valeria Taylor. 232 pp. Love and
romance on poverty row. ISBN 0-941483-41-X 8.95

PLEASURES by Robbi Sommers. 204 pp. Unprecedented
eroticism. ISBN 0-941483-49-5 8.95

EDGEWISE by Camarin Grae. 372 pp. Spellbinding
adventure. ISBN 0-941483-19-3 9.95

FATAL REUNION by Claire McNab. 216 pp. 2nd Det. Inspec.
Carol Ashton mystery. ISBN 0-941483-40-1 8.95

KEEP TO ME STRANGER by Sarah Aldridge. 372 pp. Romance
set in a department store dynasty. ISBN 0-941483-38-X 9.95

HEARTSCAPE by Sue Gambill. 204 pp. American lesbian in
Portugal. ISBN 0-941483-33-9 8.95

IN THE BLOOD by Lauren Wright Douglas. 252 pp. Lesbian
science fiction adventure fantasy ISBN 0-941483-22-3 8.95

THE BEE'S KISS by Shirley Verel. 216 pp. Delicate, delicious
romance. ISBN 0-941483-36-3 8.95

RAGING MOTHER MOUNTAIN by Pat Emmerson. 264 pp.
Furosa Firechild's adventures in Wonderland. ISBN 0-941483-35-5 8.95

IN EVERY PORT by Karin Kallmaker. 228 pp. Jessica's sexy,
adventuresome travels. ISBN 0-941483-37-7 8.95

OF LOVE AND GLORY by Evelyn Kennedy. 192 pp. Exciting
WWII romance. ISBN 0-941483-32-0 8.95

CLICKING STONES by Nancy Tyler Glenn. 288 pp. Love
transcending time. ISBN 0-941483-31-2 8.95

SURVIVING SISTERS by Gail Pass. 252 pp. Powerful love
story.   ISBN 0-941483-16-9   8.95

SOUTH OF THE LINE by Catherine Ennis. 216 pp. Civil War
adventure.   ISBN 0-941483-29-0   8.95

WOMAN PLUS WOMAN by Dolores Klaich. 300 pp. Supurb
Lesbian overview.   ISBN 0-941483-28-2   9.95

SLOW DANCING AT MISS POLLY'S by Sheila Ortiz Taylor.
96 pp. Lesbian Poetry   ISBN 0-941483-30-4   7.95

DOUBLE DAUGHTER by Vicki P. McConnell. 216 pp. A Nyla
Wade Mystery, third in the series.   ISBN 0-941483-26-6   8.95

HEAVY GILT by Delores Klaich. 192 pp. Lesbian detective/
disappearing homophobes/upper class gay society.

                                        ISBN 0-941483-25-8   8.95

THE FINER GRAIN by Denise Ohio. 216 pp. Brilliant young
college lesbian novel.   ISBN 0-941483-11-8   8.95

THE AMAZON TRAIL by Lee Lynch. 216 pp. Life, travel & lore
of famous lesbian author.   ISBN 0-941483-27-4   8.95

HIGH CONTRAST by Jessie Lattimore. 264 pp. Women of the
Crystal Palace.   ISBN 0-941483-17-7   8.95

OCTOBER OBSESSION by Meredith More. Josie's rich, secret
Lesbian life.   ISBN 0-941483-18-5   8.95

LESBIAN CROSSROADS by Ruth Baetz. 276 pp. Contemporary
Lesbian lives.   ISBN 0-941483-21-5   9.95

BEFORE STONEWALL: THE MAKING OF A GAY AND
LESBIAN COMMUNITY by Andrea Weiss & Greta Schiller.
96 pp., 25 illus.   ISBN 0-941483-20-7   7.95

WE WALK THE BACK OF THE TIGER by Patricia A. Murphy.
192 pp. Romantic Lesbian novel/beginning women's movement.
                                        ISBN 0-941483-13-4   8.95

SUNDAY'S CHILD by Joyce Bright. 216 pp. Lesbian athletics, at
last the novel about sports.   ISBN 0-941483-12-6   8.95

OSTEN'S BAY by Zenobia N. Vole. 204 pp. Sizzling adventure
romance set on Bonaire.   ISBN 0-941483-15-0   8.95

LESSONS IN MURDER by Claire McNab. 216 pp. 1st Det. Inspec.
Carol Ashton mystery — erotic tension!. ISBN 0-941483-14-2   8.95

YELLOWTHROAT by Penny Hayes. 240 pp. Margarita, bandit,
kidnaps Julia.   ISBN 0-941483-10-X   8.95

SAPPHISTRY: THE BOOK OF LESBIAN SEXUALITY by
Pat Califia. 3d edition, revised. 208 pp. ISBN 0-941483-24-X   8.95

CHERISHED LOVE by Evelyn Kennedy. 192 pp. Erotic
Lesbian love story.   ISBN 0-941483-08-8   8.95

SOUL SNATCHER by Camarin Grae. 224 pp. A puzzle, an
adventure, a mystery — Lesbian romance.   ISBN 0-930044-90-8   8.95

THE LOVE OF GOOD WOMEN by Isabel Miller. 224 pp.
Long-awaited new novel by the author of the beloved *Patience
and Sarah*.   ISBN 0-930044-81-9   8.95

THE HOUSE AT PELHAM FALLS by Brenda Weathers. 240
pp. Suspenseful Lesbian ghost story.   ISBN 0-930044-79-7   7.95

HOME IN YOUR HANDS by Lee Lynch. 240 pp. More stories
from the author of *Old Dyke Tales*.   ISBN 0-930044-80-0   7.95

EACH HAND A MAP by Anita Skeen. 112 pp. Real-life poems
that touch us all.   ISBN 0-930044-82-7   6.95

SURPLUS by Sylvia Stevenson. 342 pp. A classic early Lesbian
novel.   ISBN 0-930044-78-9   7.95

PEMBROKE PARK by Michelle Martin. 256 pp. Derring-do
and daring romance in Regency England.   ISBN 0-930044-77-0   7.95

THE LONG TRAIL by Penny Hayes. 248 pp. Vivid adventures
of two women in love in the old west.   ISBN 0-930044-76-2   8.95

HORIZON OF THE HEART by Shelley Smith. 192 pp. Hot
romance in summertime New England.   ISBN 0-930044-75-4   7.95

AN EMERGENCE OF GREEN by Katherine V. Forrest. 288
pp. Powerful novel of sexual discovery.   ISBN 0-930044-69-X   8.95

THE LESBIAN PERIODICALS INDEX edited by Claire
Potter. 432 pp. Author & subject index.   ISBN 0-930044-74-6   29.95

DESERT OF THE HEART by Jane Rule. 224 pp. A classic;
basis for the movie *Desert Hearts*.   ISBN 0-930044-73-8   7.95

SPRING FORWARD/FALL BACK by Sheila Ortiz Taylor.
288 pp. Literary novel of timeless love.   ISBN 0-930044-70-3   7.95

FOR KEEPS by Elisabeth Nonas. 144 pp. Contemporary novel
about losing and finding love.   ISBN 0-930044-71-1   7.95

TORCHLIGHT TO VALHALLA by Gale Wilhelm. 128 pp.
Classic novel by a great Lesbian writer.   ISBN 0-930044-68-1   7.95

LESBIAN NUNS: BREAKING SILENCE edited by Rosemary
Curb and Nancy Manahan. 432 pp. Unprecedented autobiographies
of religious life.   ISBN 0-930044-62-2   9.95

THE SWASHBUCKLER by Lee Lynch. 288 pp. Colorful novel
set in Greenwich Village in the sixties.   ISBN 0-930044-66-5   8.95

MISFORTUNE'S FRIEND by Sarah Aldridge. 320 pp. Historical Lesbian novel set on two continents.   ISBN 0-930044-67-3   7.95

A STUDIO OF ONE'S OWN by Ann Stokes. Edited by
Dolores Klaich. 128 pp. Autobiography.   ISBN 0-930044-64-9   7.95

SEX VARIANT WOMEN IN LITERATURE by Jeannette
Howard Foster. 448 pp. Literary history.   ISBN 0-930044-65-7   8.95

A HOT-EYED MODERATE by Jane Rule. 252 pp. Hard-hitting
essays on gay life; writing; art.   ISBN 0-930044-57-6   7.95

INLAND PASSAGE AND OTHER STORIES by Jane Rule.
288 pp. Wide-ranging new collection.   ISBN 0-930044-56-8   7.95

WE TOO ARE DRIFTING by Gale Wilhelm. 128 pp. Timeless
Lesbian novel, a masterpiece.   ISBN 0-930044-61-4   6.95

AMATEUR CITY by Katherine V. Forrest. 224 pp. A Kate
Delafield mystery. First in a series.   ISBN 0-930044-55-X   8.95

THE SOPHIE HOROWITZ STORY by Sarah Schulman. 176
pp. Engaging novel of madcap intrigue.   ISBN 0-930044-54-1   7.95

THE BURNTON WIDOWS by Vickie P. McConnell. 272 pp. A
Nyla Wade mystery, second in the series.   ISBN 0-930044-52-5   7.95

OLD DYKE TALES by Lee Lynch. 224 pp. Extraordinary
stories of our diverse Lesbian lives.   ISBN 0-930044-51-7   8.95

DAUGHTERS OF A CORAL DAWN by Katherine V. Forrest.
240 pp. Novel set in a Lesbian new world. ISBN 0-930044-50-9   8.95

THE PRICE OF SALT by Claire Morgan. 288 pp. A milestone
novel, a beloved classic.   ISBN 0-930044-49-5   8.95

AGAINST THE SEASON by Jane Rule. 224 pp. Luminous,
complex novel of interrelationships.   ISBN 0-930044-48-7   8.95

LOVERS IN THE PRESENT AFTERNOON by Kathleen
Fleming. 288 pp. A novel about recovery and growth.
                                          ISBN 0-930044-46-0   8.95

TOOTHPICK HOUSE by Lee Lynch. 264 pp. Love between
two Lesbians of different classes.   ISBN 0-930044-45-2   7.95

MADAME AURORA by Sarah Aldridge. 256 pp. Historical
novel featuring a charismatic "seer."   ISBN 0-930044-44-4   7.95

CURIOUS WINE by Katherine V. Forrest. 176 pp. Passionate
Lesbian love story, a best-seller.   ISBN 0-930044-43-6   8.95

BLACK LESBIAN IN WHITE AMERICA by Anita Cornwell.
141 pp. Stories, essays, autobiography.   ISBN 0-930044-41-X   7.95

CONTRACT WITH THE WORLD by Jane Rule. 340 pp.
Powerful, panoramic novel of gay life.   ISBN 0-930044-28-2   9.95

MRS. PORTER'S LETTER by Vicki P. McConnell. 224 pp.
The first Nyla Wade mystery.   ISBN 0-930044-29-0   7.95

TO THE CLEVELAND STATION by Carol Anne Douglas.
192 pp. Interracial Lesbian love story.   ISBN 0-930044-27-4   6.95

THE NESTING PLACE by Sarah Aldridge. 224 pp. A
three-woman triangle—love conquers all!   ISBN 0-930044-26-6   7.95

THIS IS NOT FOR YOU by Jane Rule. 284 pp. A letter to a
beloved is also an intricate novel.   ISBN 0-930044-25-8   8.95

FAULTLINE by Sheila Ortiz Taylor. 140 pp. Warm, funny,
literate story of a startling family.   ISBN 0-930044-24-X   6.95

THE LESBIAN IN LITERATURE by Barbara Grier. 3d ed.
Foreword by Maida Tilchen. 240 pp. Comprehensive bibliography.
Literary ratings; rare photos.   ISBN 0-930044-23-1   7.95

ANNA'S COUNTRY by Elizabeth Lang. 208 pp. A woman
finds her Lesbian identity.   ISBN 0-930044-19-3   6.95

PRISM by Valerie Taylor. 158 pp. A love affair between two
women in their sixties.   ISBN 0-930044-18-5   6.95

BLACK LESBIANS: AN ANNOTATED BIBLIOGRAPHY
compiled by J. R. Roberts. Foreword by Barbara Smith. 112 pp.
Award-winning bibliography.   ISBN 0-930044-21-5   5.95

THE MARQUISE AND THE NOVICE by Victoria Ramstetter.
108 pp. A Lesbian Gothic novel.   ISBN 0-930044-16-9   6.95

OUTLANDER by Jane Rule. 207 pp. Short stories and essays
by one of our finest writers.   ISBN 0-930044-17-7   8.95

ALL TRUE LOVERS by Sarah Aldridge. 292 pp. Romantic
novel set in the 1930s and 1940s.   ISBN 0-930044-10-X   7.95

A WOMAN APPEARED TO ME by Renee Vivien. 65 pp. A
classic; translated by Jeannette H. Foster. ISBN 0-930044-06-1   5.00

CYTHEREA'S BREATH by Sarah Aldridge. 240 pp. Romantic
novel about women's entrance into medicine.
                                             ISBN 0-930044-02-9   6.95

TOTTIE by Sarah Aldridge. 181 pp. Lesbian romance in the
turmoil of the sixties.   ISBN 0-930044-01-0   6.95

THE LATECOMER by Sarah Aldridge. 107 pp. A delicate love
story.   ISBN 0-930044-00-2   6.95

ODD GIRL OUT by Ann Bannon.   ISBN 0-930044-83-5   5.95

I AM A WOMAN by Ann Bannon.   ISBN 0-930044-84-3   5.95

WOMEN IN THE SHADOWS by Ann Bannon.
                                   ISBN 0-930044-85-1   5.95

JOURNEY TO A WOMAN by Ann Bannon.
                                   ISBN 0-930044-86-X   5.95

BEEBO BRINKER by Ann Bannon.   ISBN 0-930044-87-8   5.95
         Legendary novels written in the fifties and sixties,
              set in the gay mecca of Greenwich Village.

VOLUTE BOOKS

JOURNEY TO FULFILLMENT	Early classics by Valerie	3.95
A WORLD WITHOUT MEN	Taylor: The Erika Frohmann	3.95
RETURN TO LESBOS	series.	3.95

These are just a few of the many Naiad Press titles — we are the oldest and largest lesbian/feminist publishing company in the world. Please request a complete catalog. We offer personal service; we encourage and welcome direct mail orders from individuals who have limited access to bookstores carrying our publications.